ZT

LES PRELUDES

Symphonic Poem No. 3
Sinfonische Dichtung Nr. 3
Poème symphonique No. 3

Ernst Eulenburg Ltd

London · Mainz · Madrid · New York · Paris · Prague · Tokyo · Toronto · Zürich

CONTENTS

Preface III
Vorwort VII
Préface XI
Les Préludes 1

PREFACE

In 1848, after a triumphal march through Europe, Franz Liszt (1811–1886) had taken up residence in Weimar. The acclaimed piano virtuoso had already been given the post of court kapellmeister in 1842, however, he did not assume the position until two years later, though still continuing to concertize on European stages. Liszt's move constituted a profound, decisive point: unsettled travelling life gave way to a regular abode at Altenburg close to Weimar, at the side of the Princess zu Sayn-Wittgenstein. Playing piano moved into the background and conducting and composing became his chief occupations. Beethoven und Berlioz were at the centre of his orchestral concerts; within a few years he had helped the court opera to a new flowering with performances of Wagner's works such as the premiere of *Lohengrin* on 28 August 1850. Weimar had become a magical place of attraction: here were encountered the 'musicians of the Future', the supporters of a 'New German School' such as Peter Cornelius, Joachim Raff, Felix Draeseke, amongst others. For Liszt these years (1848–1861) were to count as the most creative of his life, because here originated numerous piano and orchestral works, as well as writings about music.

Considered representative principal works of this period are the 12 symphonic poems – a 13th, *Von der Wiege bis zum Grabe*, Liszt wrote at the beginning of the 1880s.[1] He saw himself in these as developer of Beethoven's symphonic form, but the composer also sought at the same time to reunite music and poetry in a new musical form in the literary tradition of the Weimar classics and to establish the symphonic poem, epitome of programme music in the 19th century, as successor to the symphony. In it Liszt took up the model of the classical four-movement medium and converted it into a model structured in one movement. He applied in the process a variation technique thematically: themes and motifs – depending on function and mood – are melodically, rhythmically transformed in character and thus guarantee unity within variety. Furthermore, the description 'poem' directly referred to the narrative, verbal aspect of the genre.

Liszt chose the term only later: at the beginning of 1854 he was still speaking of composing a collection of 'overtures', as he made 'a more recent orchestral work (Les Préludes)' known to Franz Brendel in a letter of 20 February of that year.[2] But two days later, the *Weimarische Zeitung*[3] was referring to a court concert under the composer's direction on 23 February, with the *Les Préludes* given as a 'symphonic poem'. With that, the historical genre step was also executed in its name: from 'overture' to 'symphonic poem'. *Les Préludes* ('from Lamartine') bears, in fact, the number 3, but was the first to be published.

Its genesis is confused, and even today this still cannot be regarded as totally clarified. Concerned, in particular, is the central question of when in the course of the creative process the poem of the French poet would have become the literary programme. The controversy culminated in the following theory: 'Actually Liszt's *Les Preludes* have nothing to do with the Preludes of Lamartine'.[4] The point of departure was Liszt's visit to Marseille in July 1844, where he met with the French poet Joseph Autran. Liszt composed Autran's text *Les Aquilons* for men's chorus and accompanied it himself on

---

[1] Of fundamental importance to the topic: Detlef Altenburg, article, 'Liszt', in: *MGG2P*, Vol.11 (Kassel, Basel, etc., 2004), cols. 203–311; Alan Walker et al: article, 'Liszt', at: *Grove Music Online* [posted: 29.03.2011]

[2] Letter to Franz Brendel of 20 February 1854, quoted from *Franz Liszt's Briefe*, compiled and ed. La Mara, Vol.I: *Von Paris bis Rom* ['From Paris to Rome'] (Leipzig, 1893), 150

[3] *Weimarische Zeitung* No. 45 of 22 February 1854

[4] Alexander Maine, 'Liszt after Lamartine: "Les Préludes"', in: *Music & Letters* 60 (1979), 133–148, here 133

the piano at the premiere on 6 August. Three other choruses, presumably never performed, came along later during a concert tour to the Iberian Peninsula in 1845. Liszt compiled the pieces as *Les quatre élémens*. His copyist and assistant, August Conradi, looked after the instrumentation in accordance, of course, with Liszt's precise instructions. In 1852, the composer wrote the poet that he was considering a long overture. The earliest sources of this work – with motifs from the four choruses for men – are lost, but the first sketches may go back to the 1840s.[5] Extant are a set of parts and a score produced later by Joachim Raff who succeeded Conradi as Liszt's assistant. This material may have formed the basis of a performance, not verified by sources, in an 'Academy Concert' in Jena at the start of the 1850s.[6] Research has meanwhile proved that Raff exaggerated his contribution to the orchestration of Liszt works:[7] Liszt gave very exact instructions as to how his assistant was to do the orchestrating in copies and fair copies.

Liszt dropped the plan to finish orchestrating and bring to a close the four choruses for men, *Les quatre élémens* – the first Liszt biographer (and Liszt pupil) Lina Ramann posited that this was because of the 'weakness of the poem'.[8] After a longer period, though at the earliest in November 1853,[9] he began to rework the overture – in great haste,[10] and with the assistance of his pupil Hans von Bronsart. The changes were far-reaching, concerning the proportions of the individual sections, the formation of the thematic material, the smoothness of the tran-

sitions.[11] We can only speculate about the haste: he needed a work for the scheduled benefit concert on 23 February 1854 in the court theatre or, as Lamartine supposed, he had in mind a birthday present for the Princess zu Sayn-Wittgenstein?[12] The premiere of *Les Préludes* was placed at the end of the concert which was given for the 'benefit of the pension fund for widows and orphans of deceased members of the Hofkapelle';[13] preceding it was – in a typically conglomerate programme of the time – Schumann's Symphony No. 4 and his Concert Piece for Four Horns, solo movements from Handel's *Messiah* and Rossini's *Semiramis*, the famous Bach *Chaconne* for violin solo and the Liszt men's chorus, *An die Künstler*.

Before publication of *Les Préludes* as 'Symphonic Poem No. 3', Liszt put together versions for piano duet and piano duo – changes in these versions found their way into the full score published in 1856 by Breitkopf & Härtel in Leipzig; five other works of this genre followed, all still in the same year.

When – and why after all – did Franz Liszt associate the overture to *Les quatre élémens* with the poem of the French poet Alphonse de Lamartine, the fifth poem from his *Nouvelles Méditations* of 1823? This intriguing question must remain unanswered owing to the inadequate source situation. It is certain that the composer, in 1846 or 1847 already, had been preoccupied with the poet's 375-line poem *Les Préludes*, for the title shows up, in addition to others, in a sketch book.[14] And after Liszt had given up the male-chorus project, its overture was, so to speak, programmatically 'orphaned'. Lamartine's poem may well have conveniently come to him as a replacement, in its formal conception, its change of moods, best suited after all to the music already available. Four different versions of the programme itself exist: a very extensive one from the hand of the

[5] Andrew Bonner, 'Liszt's *Les Préludes* and *Les Quatre Élémens*: A Reinvestigation', in: *19th Century Music* 10 (1986), 95–107, here 100
[6] Peter Raabe, *Franz Liszt*, Stuttgart, 1931, 2nd enlarged issue, (Tutzing, 1968), Vol.2, 299
[7] Paul A. Bertagnolli, 'Amanuensis or Author? The Liszt-Raff-Collaboration Revisited', in: *19th Century Music* 26 (2002), 23–51
[8] Lina Ramann, *Franz Liszt. Als Künstler und Mensch*, Vol.2 (Leipzig, 1880), 304
[9] Article, 'Les préludes (Franz Liszt)', in: *Wikipedia*, http://en.wikipedia.org/wiki/Les_Preludes [posted: 27.03.2011]
[10] 'seemingly done in great haste' – Bonner, loc.cit., 102

[11] Bonner, loc.cit., 103
[12] *Wikipedia*, article, 'Les Préludes (Franz Liszt)', loc.cit.
[13] *Weimarische Zeitung* No. 45 from 22 February 1854
[14] Bonner, loc.cit., 107

Princess zu Sayn-Wittgenstein for the Weimar premiere, which – drastically curtailed – was also used for the 1856 published version; another from 6 December 1855 for a Berlin performance, presumably likewise written by the composer's long-time companion, but probably authorized by Liszt, who was himself conducting; and one from 30 April 1860, written by Hans von Bülow without reference to Lamartine.

Even if Lamartine's *Les Préludes* had not been – as explained – the model for the programme, the poem still goes ideally with Liszt's Music: the poetic version like the musical version contain – framed by prologue and epilogue – four main parts that are connected by transitions. The sections correspond atmospherically, even when with Liszt the two last parts are characteristically 'interchanged': The subject deals with the love, fate, idylls and combat of a fictive hero. The following analyses of the themes, motifs and formal elements thus present only an additional interpretation that verifies, though, how closely poetry and music correspond.

The prologue presents the opening theme after two pizzicato chords:

This is repeatedly transformed in the future course, changing character this way in the fanfare motif within the introduction:

This is the theme that gained infamous notoriety during the Nazi period in Germany: as the so-called 'Russian Fanfare' on the 'Pan-German Radio', it introduced special bulletins of the *Wehrmacht* Supreme Command during the Russian campaign in 1941. The core motif – with one other – also gives a description of the basic topic of the first principal part, of love, happiness and illusions:

The portrayal of the assaults and shocks of life is likewise introduced by a theme variation providing on the side another fanfare theme:

The reflective, pastoral section reveals its own theme and goes back again to melodic material of the first section:

Even the last section, the portrayal of war, uses and transforms what is already established melodically, in conjunction with a march theme:

The return of the fanfare theme in the epilogue draws formally from the prologue and then ends the work with a triumphal concluding apotheosis in radiant C major.

Les Préludes enjoyed a great success after its premiere, even having to be repeated occasionally in concerts. On the other hand, the musical criticism of the time did not always judge it kindly. Thus, the composer reported to his uncle Eduard:

I have read attentively and with interest the review of the *Wiener Blätter*, which arranged for the performance of the Préludes and the concert. As I had told you in advance, the doctrinaire Hanslick could not be favourable to me; his article is perfidious, but on the whole respectable. [...] For example, several dozen critics, *experts*, have already fallen upon my Préludes [...], in order to ruin me completely as composer.

But he was not be swayed, especially as he viewed his symphonic poems only as the '*Prelude* to my compositional career'.[15]

Wolfgang Birtel
Translation: Margit L. McCorkle

[15] Letter to Eduard Liszt of 26 March 1857, quoted from: *Franz Liszt's Briefe*, loc.cit., 271f.

VORWORT

Nach einem Siegeszug durch Europa hatte sich Franz Liszt (1811–1886) 1848 in Weimar niedergelassen. Bereits 1842 war dem umjubelten Klaviervirtuosen der Posten eines Hofkapellmeisters übertragen worden, doch erst zwei Jahre später trat er den Dienst an, konzertierte allerdings auch weiterhin auf europäischen Bühnen. Liszts Übersiedlung bildete einen tiefen Einschnitt: Unstetes Reiseleben wich einem geregelten Aufenthalt auf der nahe Weimar gelegenen Altenburg, an der Seite der Fürstin zu Sayn-Wittgenstein. Klavierspielen trat in den Hintergrund, Dirigieren und Komponieren wurden seine Hauptbeschäftigungen. Im Zentrum seiner Orchesterkonzerte standen Beethoven und Berlioz, der Hofoper verhalf er in wenigen Jahren zu neuer Blüte, so mit Aufführungen Wagnerscher Werke wie der Uraufführung des *Lohengrin* am 28. August 1850. Weimar war magischer Anziehungspunkt geworden: Hier trafen sich die „Zukunftsmusiker", die Anhänger einer „Neudeutschen Schule" wie Peter Cornelius, Joachim Raff, Felix Draeseke u. a. Für Liszt sollten diese Jahre (1848–1961) zu den kreativsten seines Lebens zählen, denn hier entstanden zahlreiche Klavier- und Orchesterwerken, daneben Schriften über Musik.

Als repräsentative Hauptwerke dieser Zeit gelten die zwölf Sinfonischen Dichtungen – eine dreizehnte, *Von der Wiege bis zum Grabe*, schrieb Liszt Anfang der 1880er-Jahre[1]. Er sah sich dabei als Fortentwickler der sinfonischen Form Beethovens, zugleich aber auch in der Dichter-Tradition der Weimarer Klassik. Musik und Dichtung suchte der Komponist in einer neuen musikalischen Form zusammenzuführen und etablierte als Nachfolgerin der Sinfonie die Sinfonische Dichtung, Inbegriff der Programmmusik im 19. Jahrhundert. Liszt griff dabei das Modell der klassischen Viersätzigkeit auf und führte es in ein einteiliges, gegliedertes Modell über. Thematisch bediente er sich dabei einer Variationstechnik: Themen und Motive werden – je nach Funktion und Stimmung – melodisch, rhythmisch, charaktermäßig transformiert und garantieren so die Einheit in der Vielfalt. Die Bezeichnung „Dichtung" verweist zudem direkt auf das Erzählende, Redende der Gattung.

Den Begriff wählte Liszt erst spät: Sprach er noch Anfang 1854 von einer entstehenden Sammlung von „Ouvertüren", kündigte er in einem Brief an Franz Brendel am 20. Februar dieses Jahres „ein neueres Orchesterwerk (Les Préludes)" an[2]. Zwei Tage später verwies die *Weimarische Zeitung*[3] aber auf ein Hofkonzert unter des Komponisten Leitung am 23. Februar: mit den *Les Préludes* als „symphonische[r] Dichtung". Damit ist der gattungsgeschichtliche Schritt auch im Namen vollzogen: von der „Ouvertüre" zur „Sinfonischen Dichtung". *Les Préludes* („nach Lamartine") trägt zwar die Nummer 3, wurde aber als erste publiziert.

Ihre Entstehungsgeschichte ist verworren und darf auch heute noch als nicht restlos geklärt gelten. Dies betrifft insbesondere die zentrale Frage, wann im Laufe des Entstehungsprozesses die Dichtung des französischen Poeten zum literarischen Programm wurde. Die Kontroverse gipfelte in folgender These: „Actually Liszt's *Les Preludes* have nothing to do with the Preludes of Lamartine"[4]. Ausgangspunkt der Komposition war ein Besuch Liszts im Juli 1844 in Marseille, wo er mit dem französischen Dichter Joseph Autran zusammentraf. Dessen Text *Les Aquilons* vertonte er als Männerchor und be-

---

[1] Grundlegendes zum Thema: Detlef Altenburg, „Art. Liszt", in: *MGG2P*, Bd. 11, Kassel, Basel usw. 2004, Sp. 203–311; Alan Walker u. a.: „Art. Liszt", auf: *Grove Music Online* [Aufruf: 29.03.2011].

[2] Brief an Franz Brendel vom 20. Februar 1854, zit. nach *Franz Liszt's Briefe*, gesammelt und hrsg. von La Mara, Band I: *Von Paris bis Rom*, Leipzig 1893, S. 150.
[3] *Weimarische Zeitung* Nr. 45 vom 22. Februar 1854.
[4] Alexander Maine: „Liszt after Lamartine: ‚Les Préludes'", in: *Music & Letters* 60 (1979), S. 133–148, hier S. 133.

VIII

gleitete bei der Uraufführung am 6. August auch selbst am Klavier. Drei weitere, vermutlich nie aufgeführte Chöre kamen während einer Konzertreise auf der iberischen Halbinsel 1845 hinzu. Liszt fasste die Sätze als *Les quatre élémens* zusammen. Sein Kopist und Assistent August Conradi besorgte deren Instrumentierung, sicherlich nach Liszts genauen Anweisungen. 1852 schrieb der Komponist dem Dichter, dass er an eine lange Ouvertüre denke. Die frühesten Quellen dieses Werkes – mit Motiven aus den vier Männerchören – sind verschollen, erste Skizzen dürften aber bis in die 1840er Jahre[5] zurückreichen. Erhalten haben sich lediglich ein Stimmensatz und eine von Joachim Raff, der Conradi als Liszt-Helfer nachfolgte, später erstellte Partitur. Dieses Material dürfte einer – quellenmäßig nicht belegten – Aufführung in einem „Akademischen Konzert" in Jena Anfang der 1850er Jahre zugrund gelegen haben[6]. Dass Raff seinen Anteil an den Orchestrierungen Lisztscher Werke übertrieb, hat die Forschung mittlerweile nachgewiesen[7]: Liszt gab sehr genaue Anweisungen, wie seine Helfer bei Ab- und Reinschriften zu instrumentieren hatten.

Den Plan, die vier Männcherchöre *Les quatre élémens* fertig zu orchestrieren und abzuschließen, ließ Liszt fallen – die erste Liszt-Biografin (und -Schülerin) Lina Ramann vermutet wegen der „Mattigkeit des Gedichtes"[8]. Nach längerer Zeit, frühestens jedoch im November 1853[9], begann er die Ouvertüre zu überarbeiten – in großer Eile[10], und mit Unterstützung seines Schülers Hans von Bronsart.

Die Änderungen waren tiefgreifend, betrafen die Proportion der Einzelabschnitte, die Formung des thematischen Materials, die Glätte der Überleitungen[11]. Über die Eile lässt sich nur spekulieren: Benötigte er für das anstehende Benefizkonzert am 23. Februar 1854 im Hoftheater ein Werk oder dachte er an ein Geburtstagsgeschenk für die Fürstin zu Sayn-Wittgenstein, die Lamartine schätzte[12]? Die Uraufführung der *Préludes* stand am Ende des Konzertes, das zum „Besten des Pensionsfonds für die Witwen und Waisen verstorbener Hofkapellmitglieder"[13] gegeben wurde; vorausgegangen waren – in einem für damalige Zeiten typischen Mischprogramm – Schumanns Sinfonie Nr. 4 und dessen Konzertstück für vier Hörner, solistische Sätze aus Händels *Messias* und Rossinis *Semiramis*, die berühmte Bach-*Chaconne* für Violine solo und der Liszt'sche Männerchor *An die Künstler*.

Vor der Drucklegung der *Préludes* als „Sinfonische Dichtung Nr. 3" erstellte Liszt Fassungen für Klavier zu vier Händen und für zwei Klaviere – Änderungen in diesen Versionen fanden Eingang in die 1856 von Breitkopf & Härtel in Leipzig publizierte Partitur, der noch fünf weitere Werke dieser Gattung im gleichen Jahr folgten.

Wann – und warum überhaupt – hat Franz Liszt die Ouvertüre zu *Les quatre élémens* mit der Dichtung des französischen Dichters Alphonse de Lamartine, dem fünften Gedicht aus den *Nouvelles Méditations* von 1823, in Verbindung gebracht? Diese spannende Frage muss wegen der dürftigen Quellenlage unbeantwortet bleiben. Fest steht, dass sich der Komponist bereits 1846 oder 1847 mit des Dichters 375 Zeilen umfassendem Gedicht *Les Préludes* beschäftigt hatte, denn der Titel tauchte, neben anderen, in einem Skizzenbuch auf[14]. Und nachdem Liszt das Männerchor-Projekt aufgegeben hatte, war deren Ouvertüre programmatisch so-

[5] Andrew Bonner: „Liszt's *Les Préludes* and *Les Quatre Élémens*: A Reinvestigation", in: *19th Century Music* 10 (1986), S. 95–107, hier: S. 100.
[6] Peter Raabe: *Franz Liszt*, Stuttgart 1931, 2. ergänzte Aufl. Tutzing 1968, Bd. 2, S. 299.
[7] Paul A. Bertagnolli: „Amanuensis or Author? The Liszt-Raff-Collaboration Revisted", in: *19th Century Music* 26 (2002), S. 23–51.
[8] Lina Ramann: *Franz Liszt. Als Künstler und Mensch*, Band 2, Leipzig 1880, S. 304.
[9] Art. „Les préludes (Franz Liszt)", in: *Wikipedia*, http://en.wikipedia.org/wiki/Les_Preludes [Aufruf: 27.03.2011].
[10] „seemingly done in great haste" – Bonner, a. a. O., S. 102.
[11] Bonner, a. a. O., S. 103.
[12] *Wikipedia*, Art. „Les Préludes (Franz Liszt)", a. a. O.
[13] *Weimarische Zeitung* Nr. 45 vom 22. Februar 1854.
[14] Bonner, a. a. O., S. 107.

zusagen „verwaist". Als Ersatz kam ihm wohl Lamartines Gedicht gelegen, eignete es sich doch bestens in seiner formalen Anlage, seinem Wechsel der Stimmungen zur bereits vorliegenden Musik. Vom Programm selbst existieren vier verschiedene Versionen: eine sehr umfangreiche von der Hand der Fürstin zu Sayn-Wittgenstein für die Weimarer Uraufführung, die – drastisch gekürzt – auch für die Druckversion 1856 verwendet wurde, eine weitere vom 6. Dezember 1855 für eine Berliner Aufführung, vermutlich ebenfalls von der Lebensgefärtin des Komponisten verfasst, wohl aber von Liszt, der selbst dirigierte, autorisiert, und eine vom 30. April 1860, geschrieben von Hans von Bülow, ohne Verweis auf Lamartine.

Auch wenn Lamartines *Les Préludes* nicht – wie dargelegt – Vorlage für das Programm gewesen war, passt es doch ideal zur Musik von Franz Liszt: Poetische wie musikalische Version umfassen – von Prolog und Epilog umrahmt – vier Hauptteile, die durch Überleitungen verbunden sind. Auch stimmungsmäßig entsprechen sich Abschnitte, selbst wenn die beiden letzten Teile charaktermäßig bei Liszt „vertauscht" sind: Das Sujet handelt von Liebe, Schicksal, Idylle und Kampf eines fiktiven Helden. Die folgende Analyse der Themen, Motive und Formelemente stellt also nur eine nachträgliche Interpretation dar, die allerdings belegt, wie eng Poesie und Musik korrespondieren.

Der Prolog präsentiert nach zwei Pizzikato-Akkorden das Eingangsthema:

Dieses wird in der Folge immer wieder transformiert, ändert seinen Charakter, so in dem Fanfarenmotiv innerhalb der Einleitung:

Es ist das Thema, das in der Zeit des Nationalsozialismus in Deutschland unrühmliche Bekanntheit erlangte: Als sogenannte „Russland-Fanfare" leitete es ab dem Russland-Feldzug 1941 im *Großdeutschen Rundfunk* die Sondermeldungen des Oberkommandos der Wehrmacht ein. Das Kernmotiv wird – mit einem weiteren – auch zur tragenden Thematik des ersten Hauptteils, der Liebe, Glück und Illusionen beschreibt:

Die Schilderung der Stürme und Erschütterungen des Lebens wird gleichfalls von einer Themen-Abwandlung eingeleitet, der ein weiteres Fanfaren-Thema zur Seite gestellt wird:

Der Abschnitt des friedlichen Landlebens exponiert ein eigenes Thema und greift wieder auf melodisches Material des ersten Abschnittes zurück:

Auch der letzte Abschnitt, die Kriegsschilderung, verwendet und transformiert melodisch bereits Etabliertes in Verbindung mit einem Marsch-Thema:

X

Die Wiederkehr des Fanfaren-Themas im Epilog spannt formal den Bogen zum Prolog und beendet das Werk dann mit einer triumphalen Schlussapotheose in strahlendem C-Dur.

Die Sinfonische Dichtung Nr. 3 *Les Préludes* hatte nach ihrer Uraufführung großen Erfolg, musste in Konzerten gelegentlich sogar wiederholt werden. Die Musikkritik der Zeit urteilte dagegen nicht immer freundlich. So berichtet der Komponist seinem Onkel Eduard:

Die Besprechung der Wiener Blätter, welche die Aufführung der Préludes und des Conzerts veranlasst, habe ich mit Aufmerksamkeit und Interesse gelesen. Wie ich es Dir im Voraus gesagt hatte, konnte der doctrinäre Hanslick mir nicht günstig sein; sein Aufsatz ist perfid, aber im Ganzen anständig. […] über meine Préludes zum Beispiel […] sind schon mehrere Dutzend Kritiker *von Fach* hergefallen, um mich als Componisten von Grund auf zu ruinieren.

Aber davon wollte er sich nicht beirren lassen, zumal er seine Sinfonische Dichtung nur als „*Vorspiel* zu meiner Compositions-Laufbahn“[15] sah.

Wolfgang Birtel

[15] Brief an Eduard Liszt vom 26. März 1957, zit. nach: *Franz Liszt's Briefe*, a. a. O., S. 271f.

PRÉFACE

Après une tournée triomphale à travers l'Europe, Franz Liszt (1811–1886) s'installa à Weimar en 1848. Nommé au poste de *Kapellmeister* de la cour dès 1842, le jeune pianiste virtuose acclamé de toutes parts ne prit ses fonctions que deux ans plus tard tout en continuant de se produire sur les scènes européennes. Son changement de résidence marqua une profonde rupture car ses voyages incessants restreignaient son séjour régulier à Altenburg, proche de Weimar, aux côtés de la princesse zu Sayn-Wittgenstein, et ses activités se tournèrent principalement vers la direction d'orchestre et la composition aux dépens du piano. Les concerts qu'il organisa dans ses nouvelles fonctions étaient dominés par les œuvres de Beethoven et de Berlioz et il infusa un nouveau souffle à l'opéra de la cour par la représentation d'œuvres de Wagner, comme la création de *Lohengrin* le 28 août 1850. Weimar devint un foyer où se rencontrèrent les « musiciens de l'avenir » et les adeptes d'une « nouvelle école allemande » tels que Peter Cornelius, Joachim Raff, Felix Draeseke, entre autres. Ces treize années (1848–1861), au cours desquelles il produisit de nombreuses œuvres pour piano et pour orchestre et publia plusieurs écrits sur la musique, comptèrent parmi les plus créatives de la vie de Liszt.

Les chefs-d'œuvre les plus représentatifs de cette période sont constitués par les douze poèmes symphoniques – Liszt en écrivit un treizième, *Von der Wiege bis zum Grabe*, au début des années 1880[1] – qui se plaçaient à la fois dans le prolongement de la forme symphonique de Beethoven et dans la tradition poétique du classicisme de Weimar. Liszt chercha à y associer la musique et la poésie dans une nouvelle forme musicale et établit le poème symphonique en successeur de la symphonie, dans la lignée de la musique à programme du XIXème siècle. Il reprit le modèle des quatre mouvements de la symphonie classique et le transforma en un concept unitaire de mouvements enchaînés. Il fit appel à une technique de variation thématique par laquelle thèmes et motifs – selon leur fonction et leur spécificité – sont transformés mélodiquement, rythmiquement et dans leur caractère et assurent l'unité de l'œuvre dans sa diversité. L'appellation de « poème » se rattache directement à l'aspect narratif et expressif de la forme.

Liszt ne se rallia à cette notion formelle que tardivement. Il parlait encore, au début de 1854, d'une série « d'ouvertures » en préparation et annonça « une nouvelle œuvre pour orchestre (Les Préludes) » dans une lettre à Franz Brendel du 20 février de cette même année,[2] tandis que deux jours plus tard, le *Weimarische Zeitung*[3] rendit compte de l'exécution de *Les Préludes* (« d'après Lamartine ») comme d'un « poème symphonique » lors d'un concert du 23 février à la cour, sous la direction du compositeur. Le cheminement historique de cette forme et de son appellation d' « ouverture » à « poème symphonique » était accompli. *Les Préludes* (« d'après Lamartine ») porte le numéro trois des poèmes symphoniques bien qu'il fût publié le premier.

La genèse de ce poème symphonique est confuse et n'est toujours pas définitivement éclaircie, en particulier la question centrale de savoir à quel moment du processus créatif les vers du poète français fournirent le support d'un programme littéraire. La controverse culmina avec la proclamation de la théorie suivante : « Actually Liszt's *Les Préludes* have nothing to do

---

[1] Voir à ce sujet les articles de fond : Detlef ALTENBURG, article « Liszt » in : *MGG2P*, vol.11, Kassel, Basel, etc. 2004, pp.203–311 ; Alan WALKER, entre autres, article « Liszt » sur le site *Grove Music Online* [consultation 29.03.2011]

[2] Lettre à Franz Brendel du 20 février 1854, cité d'après *Franz Liszt's Briefe*, rassemblées et éditées par LA MARA, vol.I : *Von Paris bis Rom*, Leipzig, 1893, p.150

[3] *Weimarische Zeitung* n° 45, 22 février 1854

with *Les Préludes* de Lamartine » (« En fait, *Les Préludes* de Liszt n'ont rien à voir avec *Les Préludes* de Lamartine »).[4] Au point de départ de la composition se situe une visite effectuée en juillet 1844 par Liszt à Marseille où il rencontra le poète français Joseph Autran, dont il mit en musique le poème *Les Aquilons* pour chœur d'hommes. Il accompagna lui-même au piano l'œuvre lors de sa création le 6 août. Trois autres chœurs, vraisemblablement jamais donnés en public, composés pendant une tournée de concerts dans la péninsule ibérique s'y ajoutèrent en 1845. Liszt rassembla ces pages sous le titre de *Les quatre éléments*. Son copiste et assistant, Auguste Conradi, se chargea de leur instrumentation, sur les indications détaillées fournies, à n'en pas douter, par Liszt. En 1852, il écrivit au poète qu'il pensait à la composition d'une longue ouverture. Les premières sources de cette œuvre comportant des motifs issus des quatre chœurs d'hommes, dont les premières esquisses devaient remonter aux années 1840[5], sont perdues. Seuls subsistent les parties chorales d'un mouvement et une partition publiée plus tard par Joachim Raff, qui succéda à Conradi comme assistant de Liszt. Ce matériel dut servir à une exécution qui prit place à Iéna au début des années 1850, lors d'un « concert académique. »[6] Les recherches ont, depuis, prouvé que Raff avait participé à l'orchestration des œuvres de Liszt,[7] d'après les directives précises de celui-ci à ses assistants quant aux copies et à la copie nette.

Liszt délaissa, néanmoins, le projet d'orchestration et d'achèvement des quatre chœurs d'hommes *Les quatre éléments* – du fait de la « langueur du poème »[8] selon l'hypothèse

avancée par Lina Ramann, première biographe (et élève) de Liszt. Plus tard, et au plus tôt en novembre 1853,[9] Liszt recommença à travailler sur son ouverture, en toute hâte[10] et avec l'aide de son élève Hans von Bronsart. Ses profonds remaniements concernèrent essentiellement les proportions des épisodes, la mise en forme du matériel thématique et le perfectionnement des transitions.[11] On ne peut que spéculer sur la raison de sa précipitation. Liszt avait-il besoin d'une œuvre pour le concert de bienfaisance du 23 février 1854 au théâtre de la cour ou pensait-il à un cadeau d'anniversaire destiné à la princesse zu Sayn-Wittgenstein, chère au cœur de Lamartine ?[12] La création de *Les Préludes* prit place à la fin du concert donné « au profit du fond de retraite des veuves et des orphelins des membres de l'orchestre de la cour »,[13] au cours duquel furent donnés, selon l'usage d'alors des programmes de concerts hétéroclites, la Symphonie n°4 et le *Konzertstück* pour quatre cors de Schumann, des soli extraits du *Messie* de Händel et de *Semiramis* de Rossini, la fameuse *Chaconne* pour violon seul de Bach et le chœur d'hommes *An die Künstler* de Liszt.

Avant l'agencement des *Préludes* sous forme de « poème symphonique » n°3, Liszt en réalisa des versions pour piano à quatre mains et pour deux pianos. Les changements apportés dans ces deux versions furent repris dans la partition publiée en 1856 par Breitkopf und Härtel à Leipzig et suivie, dans la même année, de cinq autres œuvres dans cette forme. Quand – et pourquoi – Franz Liszt a-t-il rapproché l'ouverture *Les quatre éléments* et le cinquième poème des *Nouvelles méditations* de 1823 d'Alphonse de Lamartine ? Ces questions passionnantes demeurent sans réponse du fait de l'insuffisance

[4] Alexander MAINE, « Liszt after Lamartine : ‹ Les Préludes" ›, in: *Music & Letters* 60 (1979), pp.133–148, ici p.133

[5] Andrew BONNER, « Liszt's *Les Préludes* et *Les Quatre Éléments : A Reinvestigation* » in : *19th Century Music* 10 (1986), pp.95–107, ici p.100

[6] Peter RAABE, *Franz Liszt*, Stuttgart, 1931, 2, édition complétée, Tutzing, 1968, vol.2, p.299

[7] Paul A.BERTAGNOLLI, « Amanuensis or Author ? The Liszt-Raff-Collaboration Revisited » in : *19th Century Music* 26 (2002), pp.23–51

[8] Lina RAMANN, *Franz Liszt. Als Künstler und Mensch*, vol.2, Leipzig, 1880, p.304

[9] Article « Les Préludes (Franz Liszt) », in : *Wikipedia*, http://en.wikipedia.org/wiki/Les_Preludes [consultation 27.03.2011)

[10] « seemingly done in great haste » BONNER, *op. cit*, p.102

[11] BONNER, *op. cit*, p.103

[12] *Wikipedia*, article « Les Préludes (Franz Liszt) », *op. cit.*

[13] *Weimarische Zeitung* n° 45, 22 février 1854

des sources. Il est certain que le compositeur s'est intéressé aux quelques trois cent-soixante-quinze vers du poème *Les Préludes* dès 1846 ou 1847 car le titre en apparut, parmi d'autres, sur un cahier d'esquisses.[14] De plus, après l'abandon par Liszt de son projet de chœur d'hommes, son ouverture se trouvait en un sens « orpheline » de programme. Le poème de Lamartine lui apparut comme une substitution convenable et plus adaptée, par sa structure, au changement d'atmosphère qu'il avait opéré dans sa musique. Il existe quatre versions différentes du programme lui-même. L'une d'elles, très étendue, écrite par la princesse zu Sayn-Wittgenstein à l'occasion de la création de l'œuvre à Weimar, fut raccourcie drastiquement et réutilisée dans le tirage imprimé de la partition de 1856. Une autre fut rédigée à l'occasion d'une l'exécution de l'œuvre à Berlin, le 6 décembre 1855, vraisemblablement par sa compagne avec l'approbation de Liszt qui dirigea le concert. Une troisième, écrite par Hans von Bülow le 30 avril 1860, ne mentionne pas Lamartine.

Même si le poème *Les Préludes* de Lamartine n'a pas été à l'origine de son programme, il s'adapte idéalement à la musique de Franz Liszt. Le texte poétique et la version musicale comprennent tous deux quatre parties principales reliées par des transitions et encadrées d'un prologue et d'un épilogue. Les climats des épisodes se rejoignent aussi, même si les caractères des deux dernières parties ont été intervertis par Liszt qui fit se succéder les épisodes illustrant l'amour, la destinée, l'idylle campagnarde et la lutte d'un héros fictif. L'analyse ci-dessous des thèmes, des motifs et les éléments formels, quoique représentent une interprétation faite *a posteriori*, établit les correspondances étroites entre poésie et musique.

Le *Prologue* présente, après deux accords *pizzicato*, le thème initial :

qui est ensuite constamment transformé et change de caractère, comme dans le motif de fanfare de l'introduction :

Ce thème connut une célébrité peu glorieuse à l'époque du gouvernement national-socialiste. Connu sous le nom de « Russland-Fanfare », il servit de générique à la radio *Großdeutschland Rundfunk* précédant les émissions spéciales du haut commandement de la Wehrmacht pendant la campagne de Russie 1941. Le motif central incarne – à côté d'un autre – la thématique décrivant l'amour, le bonheur et les illusions dans la première partie :

La peinture des orages et des bouleversements de la vie est également introduite par une nouvelle thématique accompagnée d'une autre fanfare :

L'épisode décrivant la vie paisible à la campagne énonce un thème propre et reprend certains éléments mélodiques de la première séquence :

Le dernier épisode, la description de la guerre, utilise et transforme mélodiquement des éléments déjà établis en association avec un thème de marche :

Le retour du thème de fanfare dans l'*Epilogue* établit le lien avec le *Prologue* et conclut alors l'œuvre par une apothéose finale dans la tonalité étincelante de *do* majeur.

Le poème symphonique n°3 *Les Préludes* obtint un immense succès dès sa création et dut être répété lors de certains concerts. L'accueil de la critique musicale de l'époque ne fut, en revanche, pas toujours favorable. Le compositeur rapporta ainsi à son oncle Eduard :

J'ai lu avec attention et intérêt les discussions des journaux viennois concernant l'exécution des *Préludes* et le concert. Comme je te l'avais prédit, le doctrinaire Hanslick n'a pas pu m'être propice. Son article est perfide mais dans l'ensemble correct. […] Plusieurs douzaines de critiques *du métier* se sont déjà jetés […] sur mes *Préludes*, par exemple, […] pour m'anéantir complètement comme compositeur.

Toutefois, Liszt ne se laissa pas abattre, et envisagea avant tout son poème symphonique comme « le ‹ prélude › de mon parcours de compositeur ».[15]

Wolfgang Birtel
Traduction : Agnès Ausseur

---

[15] Lettre à Eduard Liszt du 26 mars 1857, citée d'après *Franz Liszt's Briefe*, op. cit., pp.271 et suiv.

Les Préludes
after Lamartine's *Méditations poétiques*

What else is life but a series of preludes to that unknown hymn, the first and solemn note of which is intoned by Death? Love is the enchanted dawn of all existence; but what fate is there whose first delights of happiness are not interrupted by some storm, whose fine illusions are not dissipated by some mortal blast, consuming its altar as though by a stroke of lightning? And what cruelly wounded soul, issuing from one of these tempests, does not endeavor to solace its memories in the calm serenity of rural life? Nevertheless, man does not resign himself for long to the enjoyment of that beneficent warmth which he first enjoyed in Nature's bosom, and when the 'trumpet sounds the alarm' he takes up his perilous post, no matter what struggle calls him to its ranks, that he may recover in combat the full consciousness of himself and the entire possession of his powers.

Franz Liszt
Translation: Humphrey Searle

Präludien
nach Lamartines *Méditations poétiques*

Was anderes ist unser Leben, als eine Reihenfolge von Präludien zu jenem unbekannten Gesang, dessen erste und feierliche Note der Tod anstimmt? Die Liebe ist das leuchtende Frührot jedes Herzens; in welchem Geschick aber wurden nicht die ersten Wonnen des Glücks von dem Brausen des Sturmes unterbrochen, der mit rauem Odem seine holden Illusionen verweht, mit tödlichem Blitz seinen Altar zerstört, – und welche im Innersten verwundete Seele suchte nicht gern nach solchen Erschütterungen in der lieblichen Stille des Landlebens die eigenen Erinnerungen einzuwiegen? Dennoch trägt der Mann nicht lange die wohlige Ruhe inmitten besänftigender Naturstimmungen, und „wenn der Trompete Sturmsignal ertönt", eilt er, wie immer der Krieg heißen möge, der ihn in die Reihen der Streitenden ruft, auf den gefahrvollsten Posten, um im Gedränge des Kampfes wieder zum Bewußtwerden seiner selbst und in den vollen Besitz seiner Kraft zu gelangen.

F. Liszt
Übersetzung: P. Cornelius

Les Préludes
D'après *Méditations poétiques* de Lamartine

Notre vie est-elle autre chose qu'une série de Préludes à ce chant inconnu dont la mort entonne la première et solennelle note ? – L'amour forme l'aurore enchantée de toute existence; mais quelle est la destinée où les premières voluptés du bonheur ne sont point interrompues par quelque orage, dont le souffle mortel dissipe ses belles illusions, dont la foudre fatale consume son autel, et quelle est l'âme cruellement blessée qui, au sortir d'une de ces tempêtes, ne cherche à reposer ses souvenirs dans le calme si doux de la vie des champs? Cependant l'homme ne se résigne guère à goûter longtemps la bienfaisante tiédeur qui la d'abord charmé au sein de la nature, et lorsque «la trompette a jeté le signal des alarmes», il court au poste périlleux quelle que soit la guerre qui l'appelle à ses rangs, afin de retrouver dans le combat la pleine conscience de lui-même et l'entière possession de ses forces.

Franz Liszt

LES PRÉLUDES

Franz Liszt
(1811–1886)

*) Militair-Trommel, Becken, Grosse Trommel treten im letzten Allegro marziale (S. 65) ein.
Military-drum, cymbals and big drum join in the last Allegro marziale.
Tambour militaire, cymbales, grosse caisse jouent au dernier Allegro marziale.

No. 449   EE 3650

A

Poco ritenuto - - - - - -

molto riten.

6

L'istesso tempo.

Poco rall.

C

L'istesso tempo.

D

poco a poco accelerando

Poco rall.

Poco rallent.

lang gehalten

Allegro ma non troppo.

Piccolo.
E
1. 2. Fl.
cresc. e stringendo
a 2.
cresc. e stringendo
cresc. e stringendo
a 2.
cresc. e stringendo
in C.
a 2.
ff
(in E.)
a 2.
ff
cresc. e stringendo
cresc. e stringendo
cresc. e stringendo
cresc. e stringendo

26

Allegro tempestuoso.

Molto agitato ed accelerando.

sempre f

riten. (pesante)　a tempo

F.

F

riten.   a tempo   riten.

a tempo (agitato)

muta in 1. Fl.
a 2
a 2.
1. Clar. muta in B.
2. Clar. muta in A.
a 2.
ff
a 2.
f marcatissimo
f marcatissimo
f marcatissimo
f
ff

muta in G.C.E.

Poco rallent. _ _ _ _ _ _ al Un poco più moderato.

Poco rall. _ - - - - Allegretto pastorale. (Allegro moderato.)

K

Poco a poco più mosso.

Poco a poco più di moto sino al Allegro marziale.

Allegro marziale animato.

N

64

Tempo di marcia.

Militair-Trommel.

Becken.

Grosse Trommel.

Più maestoso.

P

Vivace.

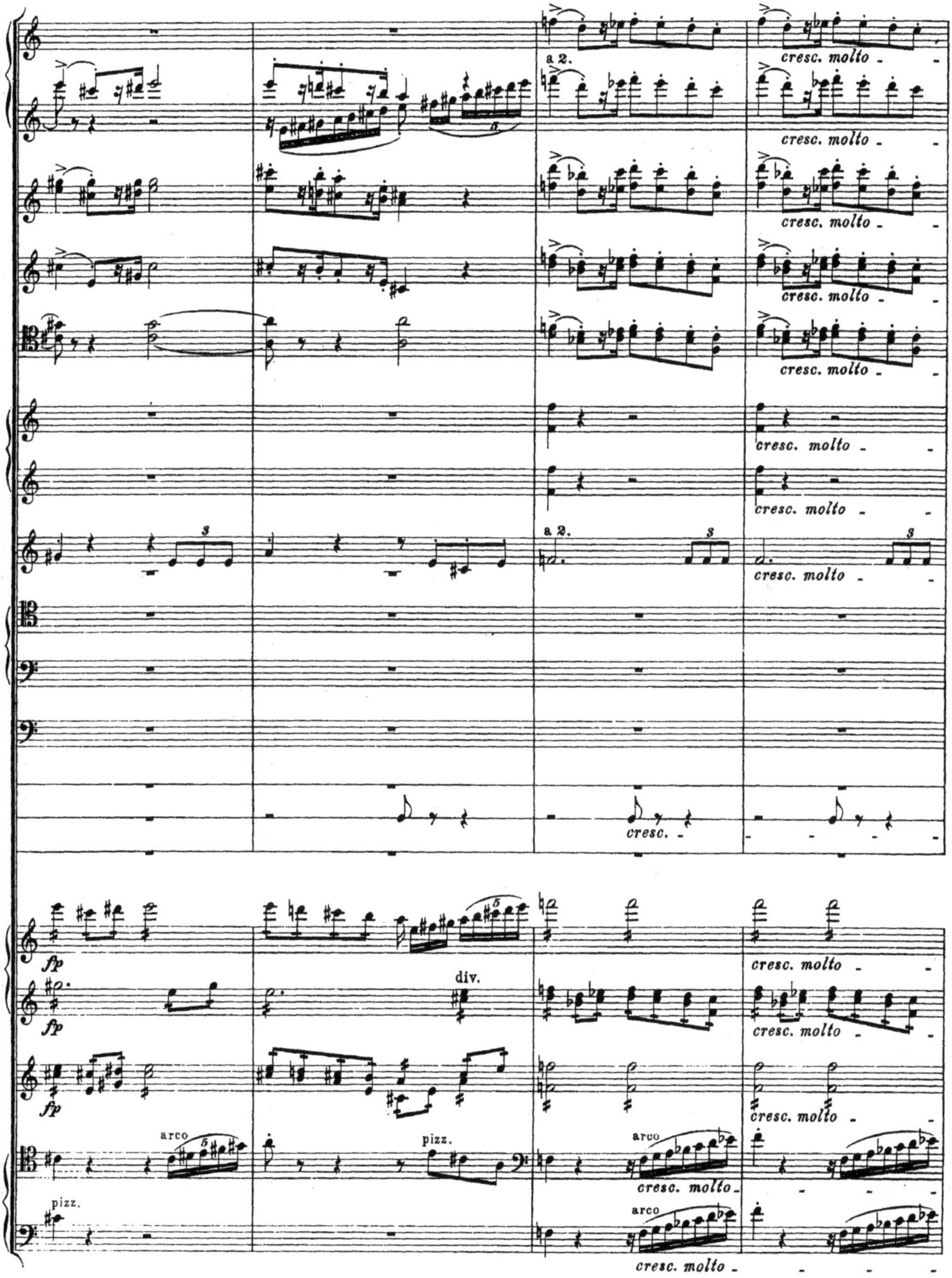
a 2.
cresc. molto
arco
pizz.
div.
cresc.
fp

molto ritard.

Andante maestoso.

molto ritardando